By Sigmund A. Lavine

Wandering Minstrels We

Steinmetz, Maker of Lightning

Wonders of the Aquarium

Wonders of the Hive

Strange Partners

Strange Partners

STRANGE
PARTNERS

by Sigmund A. Lavine

Illustrated by Gloria Stevens

LITTLE, BROWN & COMPANY

Boston *Toronto*

Published simultaneously in Canada
by Little, Brown & Company (Canada) Limited

PRINTED IN THE UNITED STATES OF AMERICA

For Dad

whose partners have included Hollywood
favorites, matinee idols, opera stars and a
host of men and women who never made the
Palace.

Acknowledgments

EVERYONE KNOWS, a routine question can develop into a discussion of great length. A while ago I was asked for a definition of co-operation, and shortly thereafter found myself talking and writing to naturalists in places as far apart as Boston's Museum of Science and the Institute of Oceanography at La Jolla, California. If there was ever any doubt in my mind as to the meaning of co-operation, there is none now — for all these busy men and women took time out from their duties to suggest sources of information. To all of them I am most grateful. Were I to list their names, this book would approach an unabridged dictionary in size. However, special thanks are due to practically every curator of the American Museum of Natural History, New York City; Miss Elizabeth Burrage, Administration Library, Boston; Norman Harris, Director of Education, Museum of Science, Boston; A. A. Millican, Assistant

Plant Pathologist, California Department of Agriculture; A. L. Rand, Chicago Natural History Museum, and the ever-obliging Leonard P. Schultz, Curator of Fishes, Smithsonian Institution.

SIGMUND A. LAVINE

Contents

Strange Partners

I

Nature's Wonderful School

FIELDS AND FORESTS make a fascinating class-room and nature is a wonderful teacher. By paying close attention to her, man has observed much that has enabled him to lead a richer life. Perhaps the most important of all the information he has acquired from watching the various activities of the creatures of the wild is a full understanding of the value of co-operation — working with others for mutual benefit.

It took human beings a long time to realize that they could accomplish far more if they combined their individual knowledge and skills. Yet all about them were examples of partnerships between animal and animal, plant and animal, and plant and plant. Our ancestors were so busy tilling the soil, hunting game and defending their homes that they had little time to notice these associations. But even uncivilized man must have seen that wolves hunted in packs, deer banded together for protection, and musk oxen employed group defense. When a herd of musk oxen is attacked, the males form a circle, standing shoulder to shoulder. Behind this solid wall of horns the cows and calves have little to fear from an enemy.

Slowly men learned the value of working together and the meaning of co-operation. At first they helped only members of their own tribe, neither wondering nor caring what neighboring tribes were doing. Gradually they realized that if they all joined forces, they could accomplish far more. Slowly the idea of working with one's neigh-

EIDER DUCK   PENGUINS   MUSK OX

bor for the common good became widespread.
Speed of transportation and communication now
makes all nations neighbors; co-operation is essen-
tial for survival in our modern world. Today no
individual or nation can exist without the help of
others.

This is why men of all races and faiths signed
the United Nations Charter. Aimed at promoting
international peace and security, the UN is man's
finest attempt at co-operation. Through its many
agencies, people of one country share their knowledge and experiences with those of other nations.
No longer does any country have to fight disease,
fire, flood, illiteracy and starvation alone. Now
teams of experts work under UN supervision to
bring help whenever and wherever it is needed.
Although many individuals hope for a better
future world through such international co-operation, a selfish few still refuse to aid the other
fellow.

Yet working for the good of the group has
always been common among birds. If you have
ever seen a flock of small birds noisily driving a
marauding owl, hawk or crow before it, you've

witnessed a simple example of how some of nature's children co-operate with each other. When wild turkeys feed, one of the flock stands at the side and acts as watchman. Pelicans make sure that old and weak birds have enough to eat by fishing in groups. Forming a circle around a school of fish, the pelicans move toward the center with their heads submerged. Every bird is assured a full meal.

Do you make a fuss when asked to take care of younger brothers or sisters? Many bird communities have solved this problem. The anis, a cuckoo of the American tropics, builds its nest apartment-house style. Several pairs of birds erect the bulky structure of twigs and leaves; then all the females lay their eggs in it and take turns incubating them. The males also share the task of hatching the eggs. This makes a very pleasant arrangement while each parent does his share.

Thousands of miles away, in the frozen wastes of Antarctica, penguins also band together to raise their families. Each pair of birds scoops out its own nest in the tundra and lines it with stones. After the eggs are laid, both parents take turns hatching and caring for the chicks. But just as soon as the youngsters are partially grown, they are placed in groups of twenty or more and left in the care of a few old birds while the rest of the adults go fishing. Penguins never use their wings when seeking food; they have lost the ability to fly. However, they do not need wings, for they are excellent swimmers and divers. Incidentally, although these droll birds are among the newest arrivals in our zoos, Magellan reported seeing "strange geese" while on his famous voyage around the world.

Like penguins, the eider ducks of the Arctic turn their babies over to a sitter at a very early age. Large groups of ducklings are cared for by old females while the rest of the flock hunts for food. As a matter of fact, unlike most birds, the eider does not have to stay on her nest during the entire period of incubation. If mother feels like going away for an hour or two, she pulls some feathers from her breast and covers the eggs. Insulated from the cold, the eggs remain warm until she returns. After the breeding season, people gather these feathers (eiderdown) from the nests and use them to stuff pillows and quilts.

Other animals also help one another. The dik-dik, a small African antelope — it is only about a foot high — warns its neighbors of approaching danger with shrill cries. There are many examples of co-operation among species of monkeys. During the rainy season, the squirrel monkeys of South America huddle together, tails twined around each other for warmth. The Barbary ape, whose greatest joy is raiding the orchards of its native Africa, always assigns several members of the band to perch high on the trees and give alarm if man appears. These poachers steal so much fruit that the Arabs consider them a nuisance. However, across the Mediterranean on the Rock of Gibraltar, a small troop of Barbary apes is treated with honors. Although the rock is not their natural habitat — they were probably brought there by traders years ago — the apes are made most welcome by the British. For according to tradition, England will hold the fortress as long as the apes roam Gibraltar's steep slopes.

Perhaps you have noticed that in all of these examples, birds and animals help others of the same species as themselves. This is the easiest type of co-operation. It is far more difficult to work with those who are different from ourselves. Some people have yet to learn how to get along with those whose skin or religion is not the same as theirs. Yet deep in the ocean, in dense steaming jungles and in flower-studded fields, creatures of vastly different species have formed partnerships. These alliances provide a way for them to secure food, shelter and protection.

Some of these unions are accidental. A bird that builds its nest near a wasps' nest gains protection from many of its enemies. Insects scared out of the boughs by monkeys scampering through the tree-tops are then snapped up by hungry parrots. The gigantic water lily, *Victoria regia,* that clogs the backwaters of the Amazon provides dry footing for water birds. In return the birds feed on the bugs that destroy its gorgeous red, pink and white blossoms.

On the other hand, some associations in nature are deliberate. Sometimes a species will make its home in or on another without harming or help-ing its host. For example, the bodies of many whales are encrusted with barnacles, who, incapable of motion, fasten themselves by their mouths to the sides of the world's largest mammals and kick food into their own mouths with their legs as they are transported through the ocean. In other cases both species gain by allying. Oysters gladly provide shelter for *Pinnotheres* (oyster crabs), for these tiny creatures are scavengers and pay their rent by removing waste materials that would otherwise make their landlords uncomfortable. A similar relationship exists between sponges and sea worms. Such alliances are found not only in the sea; even the harmless protozoa in the human alimentary tract earn the food and warmth given them by preventing the growth of bacteria that could make us ill.

Then there are partnerships that have become so vital to the members that in many cases one party and sometimes both cannot exist without the other. This is particularly true of certain insects and plants. When Alfred Wallace, the famous British naturalist, discovered an orchid in Madagascar with nectar-producing spurs almost a foot long, he flatly stated that there must be an insect with a proboscis, or sucking organ, of equal length. Later, when a moth with a twelve-inch proboscis was seen gathering pollen from one of the orchids, Wallace was not surprised. As he had said, unless there was such a creature, there could be no orchids of the type he had found. Sometimes man unconsciously severs a close relationship between insects and plants. This happens when a back-yard gardener uses powerful insecticides and destroys bumblebees. These noisy workmen are the only creatures capable of reaching into the flowers that form the massive violet-blue spires of monkshood, making it possible for seeds to form.

Authorities on plant, animal, insect and fish life — or, to give them their proper titles, botanists, zoologists, entomologists and ichthyologists — are constantly investigating similar relationships. They have found that many of the reports of early naturalists are inaccurate. They have disproved the age-old story that the jackal acts as a scout for a hungry lion in return for scraps from the kill. These practical men and women have also destroyed a bit of romance of the Old West, for their observations have shown that there is no truth in the plainsman's yarn that prairie dogs, burrowing owls and rattlesnakes live in the same hole.

Scientists have given Latin and Greek names to the various associations found in nature. No matter what they are called, they are summed up by the word "partnership"; however, you should know the technical names. *Commensalism* — sharing the same meal or table — is from the Latin *cum* (together) and *mensa* (table). This term is used when one partner lives in or on the other. The relationships between the hitch-hiking barnacle and the whale and between the alimentary tract protozoa and the human being are examples of this type of alliance. In many cases of commensalism the partners, who are called commensals, share the same food. *Symbiosis* — living together — comes from the Greek *sym* (with) and *bios* (life). Partners in such associations are called symbionts. This relationship is usually a matter of life or death. The orchid and the moth illustrate this, as does the interdependence of the bumblebee and monkshood. When an alliance is formed for the purpose of shelter, it is called a *spatial relationship* — the partners share the same space. The apartment-building anis illustrate this type of partnership. Finally, there is the union that is not a true partnership because one party gains nothing and may actually suffer. This is called *parasitism* — from the Greek *para* (beside) and *sitos* (food). The simplest example of parasitism is a flea on a dog. In all cases parasites are like those humans who want something for nothing and refuse to help their fellows.

Would you like to see some of the strange partnerships in nature? In order to do so you'll have to climb up steep mountainsides, descend to the ocean's bottom, and scramble along the rush-lined banks of rivers. Your journey will carry you from the sun-baked veldt of Africa to the frozen muskeg swamps of the Arctic. But when the trip is over, you'll understand how vitally important co-operation in nature is.

2

Strange Partnerships Aboveground

WHERE SHOULD YOU BEGIN your search for strange partners? They are found everywhere — above and below the earth's surface and under its waters. Thus it will be best if you make three separate expeditions. As cases of commensalism, symbiosis, parasitism and spatial relationships aboveground are the easiest to observe, why not investigate them first? Moreover, tools are required to unearth the unusual unions found underground, while a deep-sea diving outfit must be worn while watching the activities of the associates who dwell on the ocean floor. But no special equipment is necessary to study the partnerships aboveground. All that you need is patience and keen eyesight.

Flying Toothpicks

No one knows when the custom of brushing teeth first began, but long before mankind acquired the habit, Egyptian crocodiles were having theirs cleaned every day! The brave dentist who enters the broad snout of the largest living reptile to work on its numerous vicious-looking teeth is a species of plover. This long-legged bird is first cousin to the sandpipers you may have seen flitting along a seaside beach. When Herodotus, the "Father of History" and one of the first naturalists, reported about 450 B.C. having seen this feathered dentist at work, few believed him. However, modern scientists have confirmed his account and discovered the reason for this symbiosis.

CROCODILE AND PLOVER   RATEL AND HONEY GUIDE

Naturalists say that this strange relationship between bird and beast arises because much of the crocodile's food lodges between its formidable teeth, while leeches and other parasites fasten on its mouth. The plover pick out these pests and the uneaten food. They pay for their meal by warning the crocodile of approaching danger, squawking loudly as they fly away. Because the huge reptiles spend much of the day in the sun with their mouths open, the birds find cleaning their teeth a simple task. They never have to say, "Open wider, please!"

The ancient Egyptians considered crocodiles sacred animals and honored them by placing gold rings around their bodies. They also set precious stones in their ears and fastened bracelets on their feet. These pampered pets were kept in pools and fed a special diet of cake, roast meat and hot wine. The only attention they did not receive was the daily cleaning of their teeth they enjoyed before capture. No Egyptian had the courage to substitute for *Pluvianus aegyptus,* the plover who fearlessly hops in and out of the crocodile's mouth — the most unusual dentist in the world.

A "Sweet" Friendship

Many animals are fond of honey. Do you remember the delightful song of Winnie-the-Pooh: "Isn't it funny how a bear likes honey?" Actually, no four-legged creature has a sweeter tooth than the ratel. This animal, midway between the badger and the weasel, is a native of Africa and India. In color he looks much like a skunk. Despite his small size, larger animals avoid the ratel because of his fighting skill with claws and teeth. Yet he has a constant companion, the *Indicator major,* popularly known as the honey guide. This small bird enjoys honeycomb just as much as the ratel does, so bird and beast work together to assure themselves a steady supply of their favorite sweet.

This is an excellent example of symbiosis. The honey guide's keen eyes make locating a colony of wild bees a simple matter; but armed only with a short bill, it is incapable of picking a hive to pieces, and its covering of dull brown feathers, tinged with yellow, is no protection against an angry swarm of bees. On the other hand, the ratel's powerful claws make short work of a hive, while its tough hide cannot be pierced by the insects' stingers. When a honey guide locates a hive it calls out to attract the ratel's attention. The rodent then rushes to meet its partner, who immediately flies a short distance ahead, lights on a limb, and waits. As the ratel comes in sight, the honey guide takes off on another flight, crying loudly all the time. On arriving at the spot where the bees' golden treasure is located, the bird perches quietly in a tree. There it waits for its share of the booty, which it eats in comfort after the ratel has smashed the hive.

The natives of South America recognize the honey guide's call to the ratel. Whenever they hear the bird announce that it has discovered a hive, they try to reach it before the ratel does.

Oddly enough, the bird is perfectly willing to accept man as a temporary partner and leads him to the hive just as it guides the ratel. After the natives have removed most of the comb, the honey guide gobbles up all that is left — an arrangement that is satisfactory for everybody except the bees and the ratel!

A Partnership That "Ticks"

How would you like to be the partner of a rhinoceros? The chances are you wouldn't. For this massive animal (the white species of the Upper Nile is the largest living land animal except the elephant) has little intelligence and a vile temper. Both the one-horned and two-horned varieties are extremely fierce and dangerous beasts. They are so easily angered that the slightest irritation causes them to explode with rage. When excited they rip bushes to shreds in blind fury, or plow up large plots of ground with their horns. These horns are the most powerful weapons ever developed by a four-legged animal. No wonder the gladiators of ancient Rome who fought rhinoceroses in the arena during the celebration of Augustus' victory over Cleopatra were considered very brave men.

Because rhinoceroses have such mean dispositions, it would seem unlikely that any other ani-

RHINOCEROS AND TICKBIRD

mal would want to have anything to do with them.
Yet these huge residents of tropical Asia and
Africa form half of one of the strangest partnerships in nature. The other half is the tickbird, a
small creature about the size of a starling. This
bird is friendly with all species of rhinoceros. It
rides their backs while feeding upon the ticks that
infest their hides. It holds on with its strong,
curved claws and uses its bill like a spear.

In return for transportation and a regular supply of food, the tickbird warns his associate whenever danger threatens. For although the scent and
hearing of a rhinoceros are very keen, his sight is
quite poor. Rhinoceroses particularly depend
upon their symbionts' keen eyes when feeding in
thickets or while napping during the heat of the
day.

The larger the horn, the more difficult it is for
a rhinoceros to see. This is because the horn grows
in the line of vision — a strange error of nature.
A fantastic reason for this short-sightedness is
given in *The Arabian Nights*. In one tale a rhinoceros fights with an elephant, pierces the elephant's stomach with its horn and carries off its

foe on its head. But blood fills both the rhinoceros's eyes, which makes him partially blind.
There are a great many other references to these
huge beasts in Oriental legend; the peoples of the
Far East were convinced that the rhinoceros horn
had great curative powers. Chinese doctors grind
the horns into a powder and use it for medicine.
It is an expensive prescription, for the horns are
bought by the pound and are valued at half their
weight in gold. The dried blood of rhinoceroses
is also used as a medication by Oriental physi-
cians.

In ancient times, many people were convinced
that a cup made from rhinoceros horn would show
immediately the presence of poison in any drink
served in it. But even a cup capable of such great
magic couldn't warn its owner any quicker than
the *Buphagus* (tickbird) informs its partner the
rhinoceros of danger.

Feathers and Stripes

According to legend, ostriches, largest of
birds, bury their heads in time of danger. This is

OSTRICH   ZEBRA   GNU

not true. But it is no wonder that this belief become so well established in folklore. When ostriches see a strange object approaching, they bend down and stretch their long necks along the ground in its direction. Like all birds, ostriches have a poorly developed sense of smell and only fair hearing. But they are very far-sighted. This characteristic, combined with their height and habit of scouting the countryside, makes them excellent partners for zebras. These "horses with tiger's stripes" have feeble eyesight but a sharp sense of smell and hearing. So ostriches and zebras have entered into a symbiotic relationship.

Whenever the ostriches sight danger they give alarm by running away. The zebras rush after them at full gallop. On stormy or overcast days, when the bird watchmen cannot see very far, the zebras take over as sentinels. The noses and ears of the zebras make suitable substitutes for their associates' eyes.

Gnu often join zebras and ostriches at water holes and feeding grounds, but don't seem to have any partnership duties. Some naturalists believe that these frisky antelope are admitted into comradeship because both zebras and ostriches enjoy their company. This may be true. There are a great many people who are always welcome because of their friendly and lively manners.

A Fruitful Partnership

The purpose of every flowering plant is to develop some type of fruit containing the seed from which a new generation of plants will grow. While some blossoms accomplish this without help, others rely on a partner. This process is called pollination. Pollen is the yellow dust that may have smeared your nose while you were smelling a flower. No fairy dust has more magical power than these tiny grains. They are the source of all seeds.

Standing erect in the center of every flower is a small knob at the top of an enlarged base. Because it resembles the pestle used by chemists to grind drugs in a mortar, it is called the pistil. Some blooms have only one pistil, others a great many. Every pistil contains immature seeds. Actually these seeds are little green eggs — their name, ovules, is derived from the Latin word for egg, *ovum*. If pollen does not touch the ovules, they cannot "hatch." The pollen is contained in sacs at the top of the stamens, which are stalks that encircle the pistils. Their name comes from *sto,* which is Latin for "to stand."

In some species of flowers pollen drops down from the sacs. In others the pollen has to come from the stamens of another flower. Wind and rain transfer much pollen from one blossom to another, but many flowers need birds or insects to perform this service. In payment flowers supply insects with all the nectar they can drink. Nectar is the sweet syrup flowering plants secrete in their glands.

Blossoms choose their partners with great care. They refuse to associate with crawling insects; these creatures are apt to drop pollen while scrambling down stems or wiggling through the grass. Some flowers have an excellent defense against unwanted insects who try to squirm into a partnership — a varnish-like coating on the flower stems makes them too slippery to climb. You may have seen and felt this substance while picking pussywillows. On the other hand, flowers gladly ally with flying insects, for they can transport pollen from blossom to blossom without danger of loss. The most important of these relationships is that between honeybees and flowers. As honeybees sip nectar, their furry bodies pick up golden grains of pollen from every plant they visit. Some of it rubs off every time they brush against a pistil. This fertilizes the ovules, which slowly develop into fruit.

Nature has done everything possible to make this partnership a success. She has made flowers colorful and fragrant and honeybees sensitive to shades and smells. No one knows how many blossoms a worker bee visits during its six weeks of life as it collects nectar to make honey. The number must be tremendous. It has been estimated that it takes twenty thousand flights, each a mile long, for a bee to gather enough nectar to make one pound of honey. Since five hundred million pounds of the golden treasure of the hive are sold in the United States alone every year, it is no wonder we say an active person is "busy as a bee."

HUMMINGBIRD AND TRUMPET FLOWER
YUCCA   HONEYBEE

Other bees besides the domesticated species also spread pollen. The most important of these is the bumblebee, the only bee that becomes the partner of red clover. White clover is the willing ally of all other bees, giving them a rich source of nectar in return for carrying pollen. But the red variety has such deep florets that only bumblebees have tongues long enough to reach its nectar, and the plant depends upon bumblebees to fertilize its ovules. Without its symbiont, red clover dies out. When red clover was introduced in New Zealand to furnish lush fodder for the sheep herds, the original sowings flourished but no new plants appeared. Then, in 1880, bumblebees were imported and red clover became firmly established on the grazing lands.

The alliance of bees and flowers is of tremendous value to mankind. If it did not exist we would have no crops in our fields, no fruit in our orchards or honey on our biscuits. Yet the importance of pollination was forgotten for centuries, although it was understood by the ancient peoples of the Far East. They even pollinated by hand, just as modern gardeners do when trying to develop a new variety of flower, fruit or vegetable. In 1793, the Reverend Konrad Sprengel of Germany affirmed the magic properties of pollen. He was ridiculed and forced out of his pulpit, but sixty years later the great English naturalist Charles Darwin confirmed the findings of the unfortunate minister. From that time to this, the great economic worth of pollination has again been recognized.

The Hummingbird's Trumpet

Plants with long tubular flowers have no protection against the ants, beetles and flies that drink their nectar but do not carry pollen. These plants gladly join in a symbiotic alliance with hummingbirds, who not only transport the magic dust from blossom to blossom but also eat the unwanted insects. Perhaps you have seen one of these living gems, its wings moving rapidly, balancing in midair, its bill thrust into a flower.

The bill of a hummingbird is ideally shaped to enter flower trumpets. Moreover, the design of its tongue enables it to suck nectar and sweep up insects. The outer edges of the tongue curve over into long tubes on each side, with tiny brushes at the tip. When the long bill is pushed into a blossom, pollen sticks to the bird's neck feathers. The pollen then brushes off on the pistils of other flowers and fertilizes their ovules.

The Moth and the Flame

"Our Lord's Candle" was the name given to the yucca by the devout padres in the brave band of conquistadors who followed Coronado in his search for the Cities of Gold. No name is more suitable for this plant, with its tall stalk topped by huge, creamy-white, fragrant clusters of flowers. These gorgeous blossoms, which bloom only for a single night, arise out of a porcupine-like base of sharply pointed leaves. Seen against a star-studded desert sky, the yucca does resemble a candle.

Just like a lighted candle, a yucca in full bloom attracts moths. It lures to its flower the *Pronuba yuccasella,* an inch-long, silvery-white creature which is the only insect that can pollinate it, although its nectar attracts many other species. Strangely enough, the only food the larvae of the yucca moth can digest is the seed of "Our Lord's Candle." Thus without the moths there would be no more yucca plants and without the yucca plants there would be no more yucca moths. This makes plant and insect absolutely interdependent symbionts.

While the hot desert sun beats down, the female yucca moth sleeps contentedly in a perfumed bed of yucca flowers. When dusk falls, she awakes, stretches her wings and sets out in search of pollen. Unlike bees, who visit all sweet-smelling flowers, the yucca moth is interested in only one blossom — that of the yucca plant. As the female flies from yucca to yucca, she collects pollen and rolls it into a ball, which she places under her chin. Eventually she gathers a lump several times larger than her head. Then, like an overloaded airplane, she soars to still another yucca plant and lights on a flower. Climbing about a third of the way up a pistil, she makes a hole in it, inserts her egg tube, and drops four or five eggs into the opening. Finally she scrambles to the top of the funnel-shaped pistil, and using her body as a ramrod forces her load of pollen downward. This fertilizes the yucca so that it will form seeds on which the soon-to-be-born moth larvae will feed. With more eggs to lay, the female does not stop to rest. She immediately flies off to gather more pollen and lay additional eggs.

Soon the spires of the yucca blossoms turn into pods. By the time the pods are fully developed, the yucca moth larvae hatch. They look just like caterpillars. Like all babies, they are happiest when eating. It takes about twenty yucca seeds to supply each larva with food until it is old enough to leave the nursery. Because each yucca pod contains some two hundred seeds, there are plenty left to grow into new plants. When the larvae are ready to leave the pod, they crawl out of the hole made in the pistil by their mother and drop to the ground. They spin a cocoon and slowly develop into adult moths. Then the cycle begins again — to continue as long as "Our Lord's Candle" blooms into creamy-white flame in the deserts of the American Southwest.

Gardening Animals

Fruit, as you know, is the plant seed with its protective covering. When fruit is ripe, many plants join in symbiotic partnerships with animals. The plants provide food in return for having their seeds scattered over the countryside. Because some fruits are not edible, the plants that bear them have to resort to trickery to secure helpmates. For example, the burdock, which is so bitter that grazing animals will not eat it, has a flower head covered with inverted hooks. Because of these hooks the flower heads catch in the tails of feeding cattle. They are switched out and drop to the ground, and the seeds they contain sprout into new plants.

The seeds of berries and small fruits are distributed by birds. Some of the seeds fall near the plant, others are taken far away, remaining in the birds' bodies until dropped unharmed to earth. Two birds share in the spreading of acorns. Blue jays feed on these nuts, but have poor table manners. They drop acorns, which are later picked

SQUIRREL   BLUE JAY   QUAIL

up by quail. Unable to crack the hard shells with their beaks, the quail hammer at the nuts until they drive them into the ground. Often an oak tree marks the site where a quail tried to open an acorn.

Many animals sow seeds. This is the reason why the prairies were covered with buffalo grass in the days when covered wagons rolled westward. The tremendous herds of buffalo — or, to give them their proper name, bison — and the grass on which they fed were symbionts. It was a most unusual partnership. The seedheads of the grass were so tough that they could not break open and germinate unless they passed through the digestive tract of the buffalo. So while grazing, the huge beasts assured themselves a constant supply of food.

Squirrels are among the most active animal farmers. These lively fellows store their winter hoards in so many places that they often are not found again. Many of the nuts they so carefully bury become trees. This is additional proof of the way wild creatures contribute to the great and wondrous pattern of nature.

The Versatile Lichen

No recipe in any cookbook calls for rock flour, but it is part of every meal we eat. This is because all animals depend upon plants for food, and the soil in which plants grow is nothing but finely ground rock mixed with decayed vegetable material. The decayed vegetable material is called humus. The greater the amount of humus, the more fertile the soil.

Rock flour is made in several ways. Rivers and brooks are among the most active mills. They grind tons of soil grist every year, carrying and dropping it over the countryside. Water also filters into cracks in large rocks, and if it freezes, it expands and breaks off small particles of rock. Heat also causes rocks to expand and break — this is always happening in the desert. The wind picks up the fragments, adds them to the sea of sand, or hurls them against other rocks with such force that they are ground into dust. In some regions of the world, the wind grinds as much rock flour as do waterways in others. The gases in the air also destroy rocks, just as they rust and decompose iron. All of this wearing away of rock is called erosion.

Although most plants live in soil manufactured from rock, one plant thrives without it. Moreover, as this plant grows it is constantly creating soil for other vegetation. This unusual plant is the lichen. You have probably seen this crustlike growth on stones, garden walls, tree bark or the roof of a house.

There are nearly fifteen thousand species of lichen, ranging from the tropics to the polar regions, where they are most numerous. The only place they do not grow is in cities, for they cannot live in impure air. Flattest of land plants, lichens lack roots and the bright green color of most growing things.

Actually lichens are not a single plant, but an association of symbionts. The partners are an alga (the name comes from the Latin word for seaweed) and a fungus (from the Latin for mushroom). Algae are microscopic plants found in both fresh and salt water. They belong to the lowest division of the vegetable kingdom. Fungi, are also a low form of plant life. There are thousands of species distributed over the whole world.

In the lichen, alga and fungus live together in a very close association. The matted threads of the fungus anchor the plant and grow around the algal cells, supplying them with moisture. Were it not for this, the rootless alga would die. The alga, like all green plants, produces food from the sun. It feeds itself and its symbiont, for no fungus can provide for itself. Thus one partner furnishes food, the other drink.

Lichens grow very slowly; it takes fifty years for a specimen to increase an inch in size. As the lichen grows the fungus gives off an acid that eats a foothold into the hardest rocks. This acid gradually softens the surface until it becomes powdered. Decayed lichens mix with this rock flour and form soil. In time other plants spring up, their seed having been carried by animals, birds, rain or wind. Eventually the new growth crowds out the pioneers who blazed the trail through barren rock.

Lichens not only play an important role in the making of soil, but they also furnish food for some species of insects. Moreover, the varieties that grow on the tundra are eaten by caribou, reindeer and musk oxen. In sub-Arctic regions and in the Orient, lichens are harvested, dried, and used for food for both humans and cattle. A lichen, the *Lecanora esculenta,* is believed to have been the manna of the Bible. The ancient Egyptians ate it and it is still eaten by the tribesmen of the Near East. Tombs unearthed in the Valley of the Nile contain shreds of lichens packed among the foodstuffs buried with the mummies.

Before medicine became a science, lichens were supposed to cure a long list of diseases. But today we believe that they have very little medical value, although Iceland "moss" is used as a laxative, while other species are ingredients in salves. Some lichens are used in Europe to tan animal hides. In Russia they take the place of hops in the making of beer. Various species are used in the compounding of cosmetics, perfumes and soaps in France. Lichens make an excellent culture for bacteria, are of use in making sizing for paper, in the manufacture of calico and isinglass, and in the coloring of fabrics and paints.

Among the dyes derived from lichens is orchil,

a brilliant blue. This dye has been used by man since pre-Christian times. Various yellow and brown dyes are also made from lichens. The litmus paper which chemists use in their tests for acidity and alkalinity is a dyestuff obtained from certain lichens.

Unlike Eskimo, Chinese or Arab youngsters, you probably will never eat a lichen. But you are constantly eating plants that have grown in the rock flour created by the alga-fungus combination. Vegetable soup is an excellent example of this; rice is a seed, carrots are roots, onions are stems, parsley is a leaf, and tomatoes are fruit.

Aerial Associates

The hanging gardens of Babylon were one of the Seven Wonders of the World in ancient times. But how astonished the peoples of yesteryear would have been to learn that some South American ants cultivate hanging gardens in trees! Not only does the location make these gardens un-usual; the fourteen plants that grow in them are found nowhere else. Moreover, the insect farmers are completely dependent upon them for food.

The chances are that this is one of the oldest alliances between plant and animal. We know that ants developed their present form at a very early period; fossilized ants are often found in amber formed some forty million years ago when dense forests covered the shores of the Baltic Sea. These specimens look exactly like their present-day descendants. So ants must have cultivated special varieties of plants to meet their food problem untold ages ago. Of course it is possible that these fourteen plants once were very common but have vanished over the years except in the insects' hanging gardens. This could be the case, for the ants carefully gather seeds at harvest time and store them for planting the next year.

Another aerial association exists — the fire ants and the acacia tree of the West Indies. It is difficult to understand why fire ants need help to defend themselves, for they are vicious creatures, capable of inflicting great pain. Their bites feel as if red-hot nails are being driven through the flesh. This is the reason for their name. Nor would it seem that the acacia could not withstand attack by humans or animals. Its trunk and twigs are covered with huge, sharp double thorns. In fact, an acacia thicket is almost impassable, even to a machete-wielding man. That is why the people of the Caribbean have nicknamed the tree *Arrete le Neg*. In their language this means, "Stop the Negro."

Yet tree and ant live in symbiosis for protection. Whenever any living thing touches an acacia, the ferocious ants pour out of their holes in the base of the terrible thorns and swarm upon the intruder, covering his body with hundreds of painful bites. In return, the sharp thorns protect the insects from many natural enemies. The acacia also supplies its partner with food. At the base of each leaflet there is a gland that secretes a honey on which the ants feed.

The Most Important Partnership

Imagine a factory in which no paid workers are employed, waste material is turned into something valuable, and useless by-products are automatically thrown away! This is no fantastic dream. You and all other animals are silent partners in countless factories of this kind, sharing the profits with green plants. This is the most important partnership in nature, for if it did not exist all life would vanish from the earth. Without it plants would wither and die, while animals would either suffocate or starve to death.

Strangely enough, the act of breathing holds the symbiosis of plants and animals together. When animals exhale they expel carbon dioxide. Green plants take this gas in through their leaves when the sun shines, combine it with water from the soil, and turn the mixture into the starch and sugar they use for food. In the process they release oxygen into the atmosphere. This gas is the source of life for all animals.

The ability of green plants to manufacture their food from sunlight, water and carbon dioxide has long attracted the attention of scientists. The process is called *photosynthesis,* which means "building up under the influence of light." This miracle, which keeps the amount of oxygen in the air constant, depends upon a pigment called chlorophyll which is found in all green leaf foliage. Nothing is more vital to mankind than this wonder-working material that makes possible the exchange of carbon dioxide and oxygen between plants and animals.

Chlorophyll cannot work well without light, but when the machinery of the leaf factories is set in motion by sunshine, chlorophyll helps manufacture sugar and starch and aids in sending countless tons of oxygen into the air. It is a very complicated process, but by using radioactive carbon dioxide scientists have been able to gain an understanding of its mysteries. They have discovered that when the sun shines brightly, large amounts of carbon dioxide and oxygen pass in and out of the pores of the leaves. These pores are called *stoma,* which means mouth in Greek. Carbon dioxide is combined with water by chlorophyll and turned into starch. All the starch made by photosynthesis has to be changed to sugar before it can be used. Some of the sugar is used immediately; the rest is stored in the sapwood for next year's growth. Oxygen is a by-product of this activity.

Carbon dioxide is always being added to the

atmosphere, either from the burning of fuel or the exhalation of animals. Yet because of the partnership between plants and animals, the amount in the air does not vary greatly. As would be expected, there is more carbon dioxide in the atmosphere at night than in the daytime. There is also more on cloudy days than during clear weather. However, the alliance maintains a perfect balance. Animals consume oxygen and give off carbon dioxide; plants take in carbon dioxide and give off oxygen through their leaves.

The greater the concentration of carbon dioxide in the air, the faster the rate of photosynthesis, which means more rapid growth and better crops of fruits, flowers and vegetables. Some florists install machines to increase the carbon dioxide content of the air in their greenhouses. Experiments have also been made in laying pipes to carry carbon dioxide over field crops.

During the growing season your leaf partners work busily, and they become very tired. If you live in the North you can tell when they are weary. After laboring all summer their chlorophyll becomes worn out by autumn. Then yellow pigments appear, which were hidden by the green color of the leaves. The yellows are followed by reds and purples. The depth of their hue depends upon the amount of sugar in the leaves. Finally, with the approach of cold weather, the leaves drop to the ground. Evergreens, on the other hand, do not change color and do not shed their leaves all at once. Small numbers of leaves fall at intervals, leaving some on the stems all the time.

The American Indians, who knew nothing of the exchange of oxygen and carbon dioxide between plants and animals, had a legend explaining why leaves change color in the fall. According to the tale told in the tepees, the sky-hunters once killed a giant bear just before winter. Some of the beast's blood fell on the trees below, turning them red. Other trees became yellow because fat spattered from the fire where the bear was roasting. Ever since that time, the storytellers claim, leaves have been red and yellow in the autumn.

3

Strange Partnerships Underground

ARE YOU READY for your second expedition? Although this trip will take you to many foreign lands, underground alliances can also be found in your back yard, a vacant city lot, or in any garden. While you won't have to dig very deeply to uncover any of these partnerships, be sure and pack a light shovel. If you are squeamish when insects crawl over your hands or if you blister easily, a pair of work gloves should be included in your baggage. Another useful bit of equipment is a magnifying glass, for it will enable you to get a clearer view of the allies who co-operate underground.

Co-operating Chemists

Imagine being in a candy store with plenty of money to spend, but you can't buy anything. Green plants are in a situation very much like this, for although they depend upon nitrogen to grow, they are unable to take it out of the air. Yet this gas makes up three-fourths of the atmosphere. Before plants can use nitrogen, it must undergo a chemical change. Then plants can absorb it from water and soil. However, the plants rarely get enough to satisfy their needs. This is why farmers spread tons of nitrates on their fields every year.

Some plants do not depend upon man to furnish them with nitrogen. They have symbionts capable of extracting it from the air around the plant roots, then converting it into a compound the plants can use. You cannot see these skilled chemists except through the lens of a high-power microscope, for they are among the smallest living things. These minute objects are bacteria — one-celled plants that lack roots, stems and leaves. Many of them are rod-shaped, hence their name from the Greek *baktron,* meaning stick. Bacteria are found almost everywhere — in air, food, soil, water, and in the mouths and stomachs of animals. Most bacteria are harmless and are very beneficial to mankind, but many others cause diseases in plants and animals.

While you cannot see bacteria with the naked eye, you can see the laboratories where they change air into valuable fertilizer. These laboratories are attached to the roots of plants known as legumes. If you dig up an alfalfa, bean, clover, pea or vetch plant, you'll find little bulbs called nodules on the rootlets. In these swellings bacteria change nitrogen into nitrates for their partners. In return the plants give bacteria a place to grow and supply them with food. With the exception of one species, bacteria lack chlorophyll and cannot manufacture sugar and starch from the sun.

Years ago farmers thought their legumes were diseased when they found bacteria nodules on the roots of the plants. Now they realize that the nodules increase growth and enrich the soil. That is why it is a common practice to plant clover as a cover crop every three or four years. When the clover matures it is plowed under. The nitrogen in the plant and in the nodules clinging to the rootlets makes the use of commercial fertilizer unnecessary the following year. Because clover and alfalfa have such a high nitrogen content, they make rich fodder for cattle. Every time you drink a glass of milk or eat a hamburger you are reaping the profits of the partnership between bacteria and legumes.

Queer Roommates

The first animals to crawl out of the sea and roam the earth were amphibians. These creatures were capable of living both in land and in water

as do their descendants — frogs, toads and sala-
manders. Next to appear were huge reptiles, the
ancestors of present-day alligators, crocodiles and
lizards. Scientists call all members of this family
saurians (from the Greek for lizard, *sauros*). Pre-
historic reptiles included the dinosaur, whose
name derived by placing together the Greek
deinos (fareful) and *sauros*. Perhaps you have seen
a picture of these monsters, which were half
whale, half lizard, and wondered at their size. But
they were pigmies compared with the Bronto-
saurus, who were sixty-five feet long and twelve
feet high and weighed about forty tons — eight
times heavier than the average elephant. However, their brains were only the size of a walnut.

With the exception of fossils, no trace exists
today of these and the other saurians that
lumbered over the earth untold millions of years
ago. But a link between these monsters of the past
and their modern descendants is found on
Stephens Island off the New Zealand coast. This
"living fossil" is called the tuatara and it resembles a great gray lizard. Its most unusual feature is an eye on the top of its head.

TUATARA AND PETREL

Once three-eyed animals were very common, but tuataras are now the only species that have three eyes. The extra eye disappeared as some animals vanished and others developed their present-day forms. However, all vertebrates, as animals having backbones are called, still have the rudiments of this third eye. Scientists call it the pineal gland.

In man the pineal gland is a reddish-gray body which is connected to the brain. On some lizards, a scale marks the eye's former location. Some fish have a third eye when very young but lose it when fully grown. Although the tuatara's third eye is complete with lens and retina, it does not function normally. Herpetologists — students of reptiles — are not sure that the tuatara can even distinguish between light and darkness with its extra eye.

Tuataras are unusual for two reasons. Not only do they show how their ancient relatives must have looked, but they enter into an alliance with birds which is one of the strangest cases of spatial relationship that naturalists have discovered.

Unlike most reptiles, tuataras do not like to

bask in the sun; they prefer to live underground. This trait makes them perfect partners for the petrel, an ocean bird that makes its nest in the earth. While fishing, the petrel leaves its home in charge of the tuatara, who keeps it clean of vermin in return for free lodging. At night, when the bird settles down to sleep, the tuatara leaves the nest.

The tuatara rarely goes out during the day. It even snuggles beside the female petrel while she incubates her eggs and feeds her young. This is indeed unusual, for most reptiles delight in dining on birds' eggs and baby birds.

Munching Messmates

Although termites are commonly called white ants, they are not ants at all and they are rarely white. While their name may vary from place to place, their habits do not. Because these pests feed on paper and wood — books, bridges, houses, utility poles — they cause worldwide damage and economic loss. Fortunately there are comparatively few species in America, but they abound in the tropics, where a single colony may have a population of three million.

Always hungry, termites gnaw trees, floors, beams and rafters. They work with the grain, so the longitudinal fibers are unharmed and the wood holds together — until it is touched. Then it collapses, leaving nothing but sawdust. Although termites get nourishment from the wood they bore into, they are unable to digest it. That is the job of their symbionts, tiny one-celled animals called protozoa. Some kinds of protozoa live in the termites' intestines, where they find ideal conditions of moisture and temperature. Unable to chew or swallow wood themselves, protozoa convert the cellulose of the wood into sugar. This provides food for both partners, neither of which can live without the other. A similar life and death relationship exists between protozoa and certain wood-eating cockroaches. When born, these cockroaches do not have any symbionts, but acquire them by eating the molted skins of older members of the colony.

Termites often share their nests with guests.

Beetles are among the most welcome visitors; they give off an oil which the termites drink. In return the termites feed, shelter and care for the beetles' eggs and young. Some species even carry the beetles on their heads to save them the trouble of walking!

The Sociable Ant

Have you ever shared a picnic lunch with an army of ants? If so, you'll probably misunderstand the naturalists, who state that ants are the most social of insects. What the experts mean is that ants live in well-organized communities. Scientific investigation has disclosed that every ant in a colony is assigned a definite task and that they all work for the common good. While this is true of some species of bees and wasps, all ants are social insects.

For centuries mankind has commented on the industry and intelligence of ants. There are references to them in the Bible, in poetry and in tales such as that of the grasshopper and the ant. Yet few people realize that ants are capable of per-

forming many of the things humans do. In any
colony there are carpenters, construction workers,
doctors, farmers, miners, nurses, policemen, sol-
diers and undertakers. Some species even keep
slaves to rear the young in well-equipped nurser-
ies. Still others keep pets, and there are even cow-
boy ants who ride herd on their own special type
of cow.

Plants and animals can have no harder-work-
ing symbionts than ants. In many cases the insects'
associates would die without the help and care
given them by their partners. There is no better
example of this than the relationship between
certain species of fungi and the leaf-cutting
(parasol) ants. While some leaf-cutting ants are
found in Texas, they are most common in the
tropical regions of South America, where plantation owners consider them a pest. They have
good reason.

Armed with extremely sharp jaws which they
use like scissors, these ants can strip a coffee,
banana or citrus tree clean of leaves in a very short
time. No human wrecking crew works more
efficiently. The insect snips a V-shaped cut in a

PARASOL ANT   LICHEN   BLUE MOTH
BLUE MOTH CATERPILLAR AND ANTS   LADYBIRD

leaf, then pulls at it until the triangular tear gives way. Holding the torn piece over its head like a parasol, the ant carries it to the formicory (nest), which may be a mile away. The journey can be compared in human terms to a walk from Maine to California with a three-hundred-pound load held high in the air! While most leaf-cutters labor alone, some have discovered the value of team-work. One ant removes the leaves and drops them to the ground, while another totes them home. From time to time the pair exchange tasks.

The nest of leaf-cutting ants is an irregular mound several feet high, twenty to thirty feet across, with entrances as large as ratholes. When a parasol-bearing ant arrives home, it packs its burden down long sloping passageways that may extend one hundred feet from the formicory. About ten feet below the surface, the insect reaches a series of chambers separated by wide corridors. These passageways are air-conditioned by ventilating shafts which provide a constant supply of moisture. As the leaf fragments are brought in, worker ants chew them to bits. Others plant the pieces, cultivate and fertilize them.

Scientists used to believe that the ants did all this in order to raise the temperature inside the nest so that their eggs would hatch. It was thought that the leaves fermented and in the process generated the required heat. Then, in 1874, the real reason was discovered. A short time after planting, the leaves become covered with a fungus that develops little nobs. These nobs look like cauliflower and are used as food by both baby and adult leafcutters. One of the most unusual of plant growths, this fungus puzzles botanists, for it has nothing in common with the ordinary mold that thrives on decayed vegetable matter.

Another strange thing about this fungus is that it grows only in the nests of leaf-cutting ants, and were it not for their farms it would die out. On the other hand, the ants would die if there were no fungus — the insects are incapable of digesting anything but the liquid produced in the threads of the fungus. Thus the partnership means life itself to both symbionts. Instinctively the ants provide that the relationship continue. On the marriage flight of a leaf-cutting queen ant, a small ball of fungus and dirt from the nest is carried by Her Royal Highness in the pocket all ants have under the mouth. When the queen has shed her wings she digs a hole and ejects the fungus. Then she settles down to lay eggs. No matter how hungry she gets, the queen does not eat. In a short time enough worker ants are hatched to collect sufficient leaves to start another plantation with the spore the queen brought with her. This gives the colony plenty of food.

Where did this fungus come from? Why does it grow only in the formicories of leaf-cutting ants? Why can't they eat some other type of vegetation? There seem to be no answers to these questions, the ants do not care. They have solved the problem of staying alive.

Ants and Their Cows

Plant lice (aphids) are the despair of the gardener and the delight of the ant. Feeding upon every species of cultivated plant, aphids have cost mankind many millions of dollars. They cause galls to form on the leaves of vegetation. They kill corn and hop vines and grape vines. They also spread plant diseases from one field to another. Among the most destructive of insects, these black, green or red pests multiply so rapidly that were it not for chemicals and their natural foes, they would strip the world clean of most vegetation in a very short time. The battle between farmers and aphids has been waged for centuries. In 1545 a French vineyard owner, seeing his crop ruined by swarms of aphids, took them into court and sued for damages. The trial was adjourned when the insects left the vines and moved elsewhere. Forty-two years later the case was reopened. After much argument a compromise was proposed. The aphids were offered a field of their own on condition that they would not feed outside its boundaries. The lawyer appointed by the court to defend the insects protested that the area given to his clients was too barren! While legal minds haggled over the problem, the aphids continued to destroy the vines. You can read all about the charges and countercharges in the archives of the town of Saint-Julien in France, but you won't find any verdict by judge or jury. Perhaps it was unfavorable to the insects, for weevils have eaten the last page of the record.

Unlike man, who tries to exterminate aphids, ants have become their symbionts. This alliance corresponds to that between farmers and cows. Just as cattle give milk in return for grooming, shelter and food, aphids give their partners honeydew. No cowboys or dairymen take better care of their herds than do the ants. They drive away rustlers, prepare pastures, and lead their stock to grazing grounds.

Aphids are sucking insects. As they draw the juice out of a plant they absorb more sugar than they need. They secrete the extra amount in tubes on their abdomen. This liquid is called honeydew. It is the favorite food of ants. Just as a farmer milks a cow, ants use their feelers to stroke aphids. The lice respond by giving off the sweet syrup and the ants lick up the honeydew as fast as it appears. Perhaps you have seen an ant milking an aphid on an infested plant. It was probably a thirsty wrangler who had been riding herd for hours, cutting back strays and watching for ladybird rustlers.

Ladybirds are beetles. In the Middle Ages they were dedicated to the Virgin Mary, hence their name. They are perhaps the most well-known species of beetle; countless generations of children have chanted:

> Ladybird! Ladybird!
> Fly away home!
> Your house is on fire,
> Your children do roam.

Ladybirds destroy great numbers of aphids and are most welcome visitors in greenhouses. Some farmers buy large quantities to release in their fields — a common practice in California. A variety of ladybird in that state has the habit of gathering in great numbers and passing the winter months high in the mountains. There they can be collected, placed in cold storage, and sold in the spring to farmers, who release them on their crops during the growing season.

While the stock raised on the Great Plains sleeps in the open, the cows of many species of ants have comfortable barns to shelter them. Some of these structures are connected to the pastures by covered paths. Ants use a wide variety of materials to construct their stables. In India one species builds an unusual shelter out of leaves. A team of ants folds over a leaf and holds it in place with their jaws while another worker picks up a baby ant and rubs it up and down the joined edges. A gummy substance pours out of the larva's mouth which hardens immediately and seals the leaf together. When the larva has no more glue, it is put back into the nursery and another "bottle" is used in the same way.

Just as human beings put milk in cans to keep it fresh, ants preserve honeydew. They do not use shiny tin containers, however. Some members of the colony hang down from the roof of the nest and in this position are fed so much honeydew by their mates that they swell until they look like small balloons. They become so full that they cannot hold another drop of the sweet sap. Dangling from the roof, these unusual cans supply the colony with honeydew all winter long. They yield a drop or two every time they are stroked by thirsty residents of the nest.

Ant ranchers never suffer the loss of having

their herds wiped out. They avoid this disaster by storing the eggs of aphids in their own nests. This is best illustrated by the care a species of black ant gives the eggs of the corn-root aphis. With the approach of autumn, the ants remove the small black eggs of the lice from corn roots and carry them home. In the spring, when the eggs begin to hatch, the ant herdsmen place their newly born calves on the roots of weeds. As soon as farmers plant corn, ant cowboys drive their stock to the roots of the corn.

Pets, Partners and Parasites

The list of insects that live with ants as welcome or unwelcome guests is a long one. It includes many species of beetles, cockroaches, crickets, caterpillars, grasshoppers and lice. All of these visitors play an important part in the community life of the formicory. Some, like cockroaches, are kept as pets. Usually blind, these creatures express their thanks for the care given them by leaf-cutting ants by licking their hosts.

The *Staphylinidae atemeles* beetle furnishes the

ants with food in payment for the attention it receives. In fact, these beetles are so content with their life in an ants' nest that they rarely venture outside. Their landlords never think of evicting them, for the beetles secrete a sweet substance which the ants enjoy. If a beetle is hungry, it merely has to ask a passing ant for food. The ant immediately regurgitates on the beetle's lower lip.

There is only one flaw in this partnership. The ants take too good care of their associates! Besides raising their own young, they assume the task of caring for their symbionts' larvae. With the best of intentions they pick up and clean the immature beetles just as they wash their own babies. Unfortunately their foster children cannot withstand this treatment; they die. Only those baby beetles overlooked by their nurses live to continue the ant-beetle alliance.

Ant nests are often visited by undesirable guests. Some are true parasites, who sponge free meals from the ants' stores and sap life itself from their hosts. It is strange that such intelligent creatures as ants cannot find some way to get rid of these pests. However, many naturalists advance the theory that these intruders earn their keep by acting as scavengers. Perhaps this is the reason no attempt is made to drive them away.

There is no doubt in any naturalist's mind, however, that the caterpillar of the European blue moth does far more damage to the ant community than it does good. This wily creature tricks ants into pulling it into their nests by pretending to be dead. Once inside, the caterpillar immediately comes to life and begins secreting a thyme-scented honeydew which the ants find irresistible. Ants simply cannot get enough of this sweet drink and the liquid seems to drug them. Under its influence ants willingly allow the caterpillar to devour as many of the ants' larvae as it wishes.

4

Strange Partnerships Beneath the Waves

ALTHOUGH MANY of the alliances formed by residents of salt water can be observed in tidal pools along any coastline and in shallow water by a swimmer wearing a skin-diving outfit, the search for co-operation on the ocean floor is a very dangerous undertaking. However, it is the most exciting expedition of all. First, you must hire a boat captained by a skilled pilot who can steer his vessel through jagged reefs and bring it safely to port despite hurricanes — for most of your investigations will be carried out in tropical regions. Second, you must buy a deep-sea diving outfit and arrange for experienced assistants to man the hoselines that will supply air while you walk beneath the waves. Be sure and check all your equipment before you use it, for your life depends upon its working perfectly.

Prepare to Dive!

The ocean, deepest of the world's mysteries, is the scene of many strange partnerships. Covering more than two-thirds of the earth's surface, averaging two miles in depth, this vast expanse of water has challenged mankind since ancient times. At first man's only interest was a surface one. In order to assure safe passage for his ships he plotted currents, recorded tides and mapped shoals. But since the eighteenth century, deep-sea research (oceanography) has become an important science. One of the results of this investigation has been the recognition of many strange partnerships between vastly different forms of life that live beneath the waves.

It seems fantastic, yet human beings have for centuries walked on the bottoms of the world's great bodies of salt water. Greek and Roman authors give many accounts of the activities of divers. From the descriptions we know that these early explorers of the depths must have had some type of apparatus to furnish a supply of air. Perhaps they used a diving bell or a crude helmet and an air hose. Or their equipment might have been merely a hollow reed through which the diver breathed. Scholars have discovered that divers from Rhodes, an island in the eastern Mediterranean, salvaged treasures twenty-four feet below the surface; so it is very likely that they had some device to provide air. It is extremely doubtful that divers could have worked at such great depth with only a reed breathing tube.

Today we can descend beneath the waves in several ways. A skin-diving outfit enables us to explore the shallows; a metallic diving outfit permits a decent of three hundred feet without feeling the tremendous pressure; assistants can lower us in a bathysphere; or we can ride down to the depths in a bathyscaphe.

A bathysphere is a huge steel ball fastened to a ship by a strong cable. It was developed by Dr. William Beebe. Through its thick glass windows he observed the activities of many hitherto unknown creatures of the sea and then telephoned his report to his secretary half a mile above him.

The famous balloonist Auguste Piccard invented the bathyscaphe. It resembles a dirigible in appearance, but the buoyancy chamber is filled with gasoline instead of helium and the gondola is replaced by a steel sphere. This fabulous device dives and rises under its own power and actually crawls over the ocean floor. M. Piccard and his son Jacques, in the *Trieste,* a bathyscaphe sponsored by the United States Office of Naval Research, have made over one hundred voyages 12,500 feet below the surface of the Mediterranean.

No matter what method we use to enter the submarine world and visit the partners who live there, our trip will be a thrilling one. Yet it is doubtful that it will equal that of Glaucus. This legendary figure was the builder of the *Argo,* the

vessel that carried Jason and his crew of Grecian
heroes on their mythical journey in quest of the
Golden Fleece. Glaucus, according to tradition,
swam to the bottom of the ocean while a typhoon
raged. Safe from the storm, he spent a week end
with his friend Oceanus, father of all the river
gods and water sprites. Then he returned home
carrying an armful of fish!

Monster and Clown

All oceans contain unusual associations between various species of animals and between animals and plants, but tropical waters contain the
most fascinating examples. Let us imagine we are
off the northeastern coast of Australia in the deep
blue that laps the Great Barrier Reef. This is the
largest contiguous mass of coral in the world. It
extends over twelve hundred miles. Some parts of
it run along the shore, others are a hundred and
fifty miles off the coast. In some places it is six
hundred feet below the surface, in others it rises
in huge islands above the high-water mark. It is

a region of many basins, rocks and reefs. The tides rise thirty feet and hurricanes are common. Only a skilled pilot can thread a vessel through the single safe passageway, which is known as the Grand Canal.

Wherever wind and wave have weathered the tops of the flat, steep-sided coral masses into sand, vegetation planted by seed-dropping birds struggles to exist, but for the most part the reef is barren. In the water, however, there are thousands of living things. The depths teem with sea anemones, fish, pearl oysters and sea urchins. Among the other residents of these waters are giant clams, whose shells are five feet long and weigh half a ton. If a diver's foot or arm is caught inside one of these clams, its shell snaps shut like a trap and there is no escape. So be careful as we set out to explore the Great Barrier Reef.

Avoiding a jagged piece of coral, we walk beside waving sea plumes and lacy golden sea fans. We are looking for the gaudy clownfish and its commensal, the giant sea anemone *Discosoma*. Sea anemones play an important part in many underwater alliances. They are found in all oceans and are equally at home in tidal pools and at great depths. These gorgeously colored "flowers of the sea" are as beautiful as any blossoms found on land, but they are not really plants. Like most submarine vegetation, they are animals.

Some anemones are merely a fraction of an inch in size; others are two feet in diameter; but large or small, they all look alike. Each has a short stem (really a rubbery stomach) ending in a disc. This disc contains the anemone's mouth. Fleshy tentacles are arranged around the mouth. They resemble the petals of a flower. Fish that venture too near the tentacles are seized in a vicelike grip, stunned or killed by powerful stinging cells, and then drawn into the mouth. The sea anemone closes up while it digests a meal. When it is finished it expels the indigestible parts, but irritating bits remain in the stomach. This never happens to a *Discosoma*. Largest member of its family, equipped with thousands of tentacles and sting rays, this exquisite death trap has a partner that removes all waste material. The helpmate is the clownfish, a tiny fish very much smaller than many species on which the *Discosoma* feeds.

PARROT FISH   HERMIT CRAB

ANEMONE AND CLOWNFISH   HYDROID CORAL

ANGLER FISH

No circus performer's costume is more attractive than the scales of a clownfish. Only three and one-half inches long, it is one of the most vividly colored of all fish. The body is bright orange, and three white bands bordered with black run vertically across the back of the head, middle of the body and base of the tail. All fins are edged in black and white. While other residents of the Great Barrier Reef wisely shun the stinging, lasso-like tentacles of the *Discosoma,* clownfish fearlessly swim in and out of the death-dealing threads. At night, when the anemone closes up, the fish rests inside, safe from all the dangers of the sea.

In return for this protection clownfish not only clean the insides of their partners (picking up a light lunch in the process) but also massage the tentacles. This helps keep the sea anemones in good condition. The fish also aerate the water near their associate. When both partners are hungry, the fish swims a short distance away from the anemone and lures a larger fish into chasing it. Then it dashes toward the *Discosoma* at full speed. The anemone lassos the unsuspecting victim, kills it, and then shares the spoil with its commensal.

Naturalists are not sure whether or not clownfish are immune to the poison of the *Discosoma*. However, the clownfish is never harmed as it swims freely in and out of its strange motel. In fact, clownfish build their nests beside their partners, actually bending a tentacle or two over the nest in order to cover their eggs and babies. When the fry are old enough to care for themselves, they also join in a partnership with an anemone. But don't envy the relationship between this gaudy-colored fish and the giant *Discosoma*. Tropical anemones can cause considerable pain to human beings who come in contact with the tentacles. Species found in colder waters are harmless.

A Crabby Partner

If you think a bouquet of flowers adds to the beauty of a room, imagine how attractive a home completely covered with blossoms must be. Hermit crabs often live in such houses. Their residences are covered with sea anemones. Hermit crabs are found along the edge of the ocean, in deep water and even in the steaming jungles of South America, far from the sea. These land-dwelling hermit crabs have two things in common with their salt-water relations. They must lay their eggs in the ocean and must move as they grow larger.

Moving is no simple matter for a hermit crab. Not only must he find a house that pleases him, but it must also protect him from his enemies. Unlike a lobster, the crab's soft body has no spiny plates for protection. This makes it necessary for hermit crabs to crawl into shells deserted by the original owners. Scurrying sideways, the crab examines hundreds of shells until he finds one that appeals to him. It must be just big enough for him to squeeze inside. After moving into his new home, the crab blocks the entrance with his claws. Now he is safe from all harm.

If you look at the foreclaws of a hermit crab, you will see that one of them is much larger than the other. Usually the right-hand one is bigger. There is a strange reason for this. Pick up a sea shell and hold its opening toward you and the opening will be on the right-hand side. In other words the hermit crab has developed a claw to fit the hole. In some waters, however, there are left-handed shells. The hermit crabs that live in those areas have grown a larger left-hand claw.

Once a hermit crab moves into a shell, it stays there until the shell becomes too small. Then the crab has to find another home of the correct size and shape. Because the crab's body has grown into the form of the shell it has just left, the crab has to find another shell of the same species in order to get a tight fit.

When comfortably settled in new quarters, a hermit crab is ready to become an anemone's commensal. Not content with the protection given by the borrowed shell, the crab wants the additional security of an anemone's sting rays. As carefully as a gardener sets out seedlings, the crab lifts an anemone off the ocean floor and plants it on the roof of his house. The anemone offers no resistance. Some instinct seems to tell it that in payment for disguising the crab it will be given transportation, and that every time its partner eats, bits of food will float within easy reach of its tentacles. This alliance is an excellent example of commensalism.

No businessman is more particular than the hermit crab in picking a partner. Some species will associate only with certain types of anemones. The bright red anemone of the Atlantic coast is seen only on the back of its crabby partner. The cloaked anemone and Prideaux's hermit crab are inseparable. This means that each time the crab moves it transplants its partner. In other cases anemones grow around the crabs' bodies. This provides a lifetime of protection and camouflage in return for a continual free ride and a constant supply of food.

Fish with Flashlights

In order to see in the gloomy depths of the ocean, the deep-sea angler fish carries a lantern! As ugly as a wicked goblin in a fairy tale, this grotesque creature is as broad as it is long. It is shaped like a misformed globe. A third of its length consists of a massive head containing a tremendous mouth armed with very large teeth. Growing out of the head is a long thick filament ending in a light organ. It looks just like a swaying Japanese lantern. Some species of angler fish carry lights on the tops and tips of their noses. They may also get additional illumination from a growth on their chins.

Most animals that live in perpetual darkness are blind, while those that burrow in the mud have very poor eyesight. But in the mysterious ocean not all the rules of nature seem to apply. Many submarine residents can produce light. This ability has a four-fold purpose: it attracts prey, scares off enemies, enables males and females to find each other, and allows the animal to see.

Perhaps you have seen phosphorescence during a rough sea or while standing in the bow or stern of a ship as it cut through the waves. This light is caused by countless minute one-celled plants that float and drift in the water. Their name, plankton, comes from the Greek and means "that which drifts." Jellyfish, marine worms, sea gooseberries, shrimp, starfish and hundreds of species of fish can light up in the same way. The blue, pink, purple, red and white shades they create look just like fireworks on the Fourth of July.

While the glow of some fish is due to a very complicated process of their own, others rely on a symbiont to turn on the switch. These electricians are luminous bacteria that live between or in the light-producing cells. Naturalists call this type of alliance intracellular symbiosis, because one partner lives within certain cells in the body of the other. In the case of the angler fish, the bacteria reside in the tip of the lantern.

No one can say for sure how many self-illuminating marine animals exist, but the estimated number is very large. Some scientists claim that luminous bacteria light up the ocean depths for fish who have no light organs. This may be true, for no known resident of the ocean floor carries a lantern. But not until some daring diver goes far deeper than the 13,287-foot descent Commander Georges Houot and Lieutenant Pierre-Henri Wilm of the French Navy made in 1953 will we know for sure. Meanwhile, unconscious of all scientific speculation, fish and bacteria are joined in partnership. The bacteria light a path through the murky waters in return for comfortable quarters and regular meals. Human co-operation seldom works as efficiently as does this strange alliance thousands of feet below the waves.

Vacuum-Cleaning a Parrot

If you have ever looked closely at a parrot's beak, you'll have no difficulty in understanding how the parrot fish got its name. The teeth of this coral-eating fish are joined together, forming a sharp-edged bill just like the bird's. It is a powerful tool, enabling the fish to bite off coral branches or sever shellfish. This unusual food is then ground into bits by teeth in the throat. These teeth are connected, forming plates with large chewing surfaces. The upper plate fits into the lower. The parrot fish is one of the very few fish that masticates its food. Centuries ago, Aristotle noticed this ability of parrot fish and wrote that "they chew their cud." Found in tropical and subtropical areas of the Indian-Pacific and Atlantic oceans, these fish never come to the west coasts of America or Africa.

As the parrot fish swims about coral reefs tearing off its food, numerous parasites attach themselves to its sides. Despite its powerful teeth, the fish is unable to pick these unwanted visitors off its flesh. So it enters into a partnership with another fish called the wrasse. There are many species of wrasse; the tautog is the commonest American type.

Some species of wrasse have thick lips which are folded in a fantastic manner. This feature is the reason why the parrot fish finds it such a helpful symbiont. With very little trouble the wrasse vacuum-cleans his partner. Its big lips remove every parasite or small crustacean that has become embedded in the parrot fish's skin. As a reward, the wrasse enjoys a delicious meal without having to hunt for it. This is a most satisfactory arrangement for both partners.

Worm and Algae, Inc.

Nearly everyone who raises tropical fish has experienced the misfortune of having his tank turn a murky green. This is due to the presence of algae. Algae are the tiny one-celled plants which were in the lichen partnership and which are found in water. They multiply at a tremendous rate when exposed to the sun's rays. Although aquarists deplore this fact, the marine worm *Convoluta* forms a partnership with some species of algae in order to take advantage of it.

This is no casual relationship. These symbionts are so interdependent that neither can exist alone. The association begins as soon as the newly born worm starts to feed. With the first mouthful it accidentally swallows untold numbers of green algae. These plants are never digested. They live contentedly in the worm's stomach and increase in numbers until they actually turn their host green. As a result the *Convoluta* has a protective coloring that enables it to avoid the attention of enemies.

At a very early age the worms stop eating any food except the algae in their stomachs. Somehow the *Covoluta* realize that their food- and camouflage-producing associates cannot live without being exposed to the sun. So at low tide the worms come out of their burrows, lie on the bottom in shallow water (sunlight cannot penetrate very far into the ocean depths), and allow the algae to bask in the sun. If you spend your vacation near the seashore you can observe the workings of this partnership. Place some marine worms in a salt-water aquarium and watch them carefully. You'll find that they rise to the surface every day, just as if the tank felt the effects of the tide!

Not all algae are green. Besides the brown type, which grows best in poor light, there are many brilliant shades — blue, orange, purple, violet, yellow and red. Red algae gave the Red Sea its name. The frequent colored rains reported in some areas are no mystery to meteorologists. They know that the drops contain the fish-keeper's foe and the *Convoluta's* companion — algae.

Walking Gardens

What animal do you use to wash the family car? That's not as silly a question as it appears, for sponges, like sea anemones, are animals. There are hundreds of different species of sponge. They are found along every coastline in the world. Simplest of stay-at-home animals, they eat whatever chance brings their way. Sponges grow in every conceivable shape, color and size — from tiny growths to mammoth masses weighing several hundred pounds. Some are soft, others hard, but all of them consist of a colony of one-celled animals. These communities co-operate by forming tubelike openings containing whips which are never still. The action of these whips forces water in and out of the sponge. This steady stream contains millions of minute creatures, which the sponge eats although it has no mouth. All the waste material is carried away by the outgoing water.

Like all animals, sponges need oxygen to live. In most cases the flow of water through the tubes supplies the necessary amount, but some sponges form a partnership with algae in order to get enough of the life-giving gas. These varieties are often green in color, due to the algae within their walls. The algae, being plants, use the carbon dioxide given off by their animal associates and release oxygen for the sponge to use. Thus below the waves the same relationship exists between plants and animals as is found on land. It is a perfect symbiosis.

Some sponges are good citizens — they help others and neither get nor ask for anything in return. In many cases they act as silent partners. Certain crabs plant sponges on their shells and claws for camouflage. They look like walking gardens. Many residents of the ocean live with sponges. Among them is the *Dromia vulgaris,* a small crab which finds living conditions so ideal inside a sponge that it grows too large to get out. Snapping shrimp consider sponges an excellent hiding place from their enemies. They are not only safe within the sponge but get a constant supply of food without effort, thanks to the pumping action of the whips. Sulphur sponges, which are yellow and look as if they had warts, have a relationship with every other creature living in the ocean. They attach themselves to empty shells and the chemicals the sponges produce dissolve the shells. This returns the elements to the water and thus helps maintain the wondrous balance of nature.

Monster and Midget

Before we leave the fabulous world beneath the waves let's look under the surface of the placid ponds, lakes and rivers that dot the countryside. Unlike the sea, fresh waters contain few associations for mutual benefit, although parasitism is common. However, algae, both green and brown, have an alliance with the hydra, a soft-bodied relative of coral, sea anemones and jellyfish.

Harmless-looking, this "minute bag with a mouth on one end" has no eyes, brain, lungs or blood vessels. It takes hours to move a few inches. Yet it is a monster, one of the most deadly killers in nature.

In their native state, hydras prey on microscopic animals that collide with its tentacles. If introduced by accident into an aquarium, they can destroy the largest fish. The hydra's tentacles are covered with capsules, each containing a poison and a hollow barbed thread. When the capsules come in contact with a victim they explode. The threads spring up and eject a paralyzing spray. Then the tentacles draw the freshly caught meal into the mouth. This organ is always busy, as the rest of the hydra is nothing but a digestive tract.

The hydra has the ability to replace lost or injured parts of its body. Many animals can do this: lobsters grow new claws, a severed worm becomes two separate ones, lizards develop new tails and starfish new arms. The hydra can do even more. If cut in half it will reassemble itself! This unique trait was discovered by Abraham Trembley in 1744. He conducted hundreds of experiments with hydras. He was astonished when he saw that a hydra chopped to pieces and left in a dish of water was whole again the next day. It is this strange ability that gives the hydra its name. In Greek mythology, Hydra was the monster with nine heads who had the power to grow two more every time one was removed. You will remember that killing this formidable animal was one of the twelve labors of Hercules.

It would seem that so nasty a creature as the hydra could not get along with a partner, but none of nature's children is independent of his fellows. Like all animals, the hydra needs oxygen to live, so it enters into the same alliance with algae that the sponges do. Monster and midget live together in symbiosis.

5

What's the Answer?

THERE ARE MANY CASES of symbiosis, commensalism and spatial relationship that puzzle naturalists. Perhaps you might try to find out the reasons for these partnerships. Don't let the fact that you are not a trained scientist hold you back. Many laymen have made valuable contributions to our knowledge of plants and animals. Father David, a French missionary, was such a person. A curious man, he wondered why no European was allowed inside the forty-five-mile brick wall which surrounded the Non Hai-tzu, the park south of Peking belonging to the Emperor of China. At last he climbed up and looked over the wall. Inside was a herd of unusual deer, the sole survivors of thousands that once roamed the swamp plains of north China. All the rest had been killed by hunters. Father David wrote to zoologists in France and told them what he had discovered. As a result the Chinese Emperor was asked to send specimens to the Paris zoo. In 1866 this request was granted. When the animals arrived at their new home on the banks of the Seine, they were named Father David deer in honor of the priest.

That is not the end of the story. Shortly after the deer were shipped to France, the royal herd in China escaped. None were ever recaptured, as hungry Chinese killed and ate them all. The only Father David deer in the world today are the zoo-dwelling descendants of those sent to Paris many years ago.

Always remember that if Father David had not been curious, he would not have discovered the deer that bear his name. So be curious, ask questions, read and observe. Above all, pay no attention to any walls that block your investigations. Of course you must obey all laws and respect the rights of others as you seek the facts. If you do all this, you may find out why some of the particularly strange partnerships exist.

Would you like to do your research in the ocean? If so, the oyster crab is worth attention. Why is it that only the females of this species live inside oysters, where they get food and protection, while the males live in open water? What the crabs may do for the oysters is another unanswered question. While beneath the waves, perhaps you can discover the reason for the relationship between certain jellyfish and tuna fry. These jellyfish eat all other fish, yet baby tuna use them as a hiding place. They swim in and out of the tentacles and never suffer harm. What does the jellyfish get for providing this protection?

Perhaps you'd prefer a more dangerous assignment. Then go into shark-infested waters and find out why turtles and large fish furnish free transportation to the remora. This sucking fish has a

WEAVER BIRD NEST   WEAVER BIRD

FATHER DAVID DEER   SHARKS AND REMORA

large corrugated disc on top of its head. The disc acts as a vacuum cup and creates a suction like that of a rubber plunger. Using this growth, remora attach themselves to larger fish. South Sea natives net remora, tie a line to them, and then let them swim freely among the coral reefs. Here the fish fasten themselves so tightly to other fish or turtles that the fishermen are able to pull both victim and bait into easy harpooning distance. You've probably read in Roman history about the ability of the remora to attach itself to objects. Marc Anthony's late arrival and consequent defeat at the battle of Actium was supposed to be due to the large number of remora that clung to the keel of his ship. Despite fair winds, they slowed down his vessel with their dragging weight.

If you prefer to study strange partnerships on land, why not take a boat trip to Africa and investigate the egg-laying habits of the honey guide? George Latimer Bates, a famous ornithologist (bird expert) claims that the honey guide places its eggs in the nest of the barbet. This small cousin of the woodpecker uses a hollow tree for a home, but the doorway is much too small for the honey guide to enter. Mr. Bates says that the ratel's partner overcomes this difficulty by placing its eggs in the barbet's nest with its feet! This may be true. Your problem is to discover how the baby honey guides get out of the tree trunk after being hatched, for like their parents, they are much bigger than the hole. While in Africa, look for a colony of weaverbirds. Living peaceably with these clever craftsmen will be several pygmy falcons. These birds of prey should, by all the rules of the wild, devour their neighbors. What is the reason for this co-operative housing?

On the way home from the Dark Continent, you might stop over in New Zealand and carefully examine the glowworms of that fascinating island. What makes them glow? Do they, like the angler fish, have a symbiont inside them which causes the light? There is a possibility that the common firefly also has a symbiont who supplies its cold light. This is a field of investigation of great importance to lighting engineers.

If your homeward route carries you through the Panama Canal, plan to visit a South American

jungle and look for a monkey parakeet's nest.
Like the anis, these birds are very social in their
nesting habits and build in apartment-house style.
But it isn't the nest that should interest you, it is
the tree teal who shares it. Why is this bird made
welcome and why do neither teal nor parakeet
pay any attention to the opossum who usually
lives in the same tree?

Back home in America, go to Texas and examine the Alamo vine which grows on the plains.
At night this plant gives forth a strong, steady
light visible for a long distance. During the day
large numbers of lightning bugs sleep on its
leaves. Can you discover if the night glow of the
plant comes from its daytime visitors? Another
alliance well worth investigating is the one between the American cowslip and the tiny green
frog known to country boys as the spring creeper.
Although the cowslip is often called the marsh
marigold, it is neither a true marigold nor a cowslip. This is an example of the way early settlers
misnamed plants and animals because they were
similar to ones in Europe. Perhaps the most attractive of all wild blossoms, the cowslip appears

early in the spring and always has one of the little green frogs as a nearby neighbor. It should be interesting to learn the reason why.

Nothing is more fascinating than the study of insects. So why not try to discover why the *Paussidae,* a small species of beetle, is found at night only on the wing or in the nest of ants. Moreover, why is it that ants can drag these creatures from one end of the nest to the other without suffering any harm? If anything else touches them, the beetles spray a caustic iodine-like fluid on the offender.

Lastly, why not turn counterspy and shadow the "policeman of the woods"? This is the name naturalists give to the blue jay. The bright blue bird warns all other residents of the forest whenever an intruder appears. It flies overhead constantly scolding as if to say, "Keep moving there — no trespassing — get along!" Is this woodland watchman just a self-important individual, a creature delighted with the sound of his own voice, or have the other birds assigned him the task of acting as a policeman?

Even if you do not learn the reasons for these

strange partnerships, your research will not be wasted. As you explore the wonders of the wild, you should get a full understanding of what co-operation means. This knowledge will serve you well in school and home life and make you a better citizen. As a result you will be doing your share to make the world a most pleasant place in which to live. For not until every individual is willing to forget differences and associate in peace with his fellows regardless of their skin or their religion will nations of the world live in perfect partnership, as do so many of nature's children.

Books for Further Reading

Baker, Mary, and Bridges, William. *Wild Animals of the World*. Garden City: Garden City Books, 1948.

Beebe, William. *Half Mile Down*. New York: Harcourt, Brace and Company, rev. ed. 1951.

Caullery, Maurice J. *Parasitism and Symbiosis*. London: Sedgewick and Johnson, 1952.

Comstock, Anna B. *Handbook of Nature Study*. Ithaca: Comstock Publishing Company, 22nd ed. 1931.

Cousteau, J. Y., and Dumas, Frederick. *The Silent World*. New York: Harper and Brothers, 1953.

DeLatil, Pierre, and Rivoire, Jean. *Man and the Underwater World*. G. P. Putnam and Company, 1956.

Ditmars, Raymond L. *Reptiles of the World*. New York: The Macmillan Company, reissue 1951.

Drimmer, Frederick. *The Animal Kingdom*. 3 vols. New York: Doubleday and Company, 1954.

Fuller, Harry J., and Tippo, Oswald. *College Botany*. New York: Henry Holt and Company, 1949.

Gates, F. C. *Field Manual of Plant Ecology*. New York: McGraw-Hill Book Company, 1938.

Gaul, Albro. *The Wondrous World of the Seashore*. New York: Appleton-Century-Crofts, 1955.

Goodrich, S. G. *The Animal Kingdom*. 2 vols. New York: A. J. Johnson, 1874.

Guenther, Klaus, and Decert, Kurt. *Creatures of the Deep*. New York: Charles Scribner's Sons, 1956.

Hammerton, J. A., editor. *Wonders of Animal Life*. 4 vols. London: Waverly Book Company, 1949.

Hulme, E. Edward. *Natural History, Lore and Legend*. London: Bernard Quaritch, 1895.

Krutch, Joseph W. *The Desert Year*. New York: William Sloane Associates, 1952.

Lutz, Frank E. *Field Book of Insects*. New York: G. P. Putnam and Company, 3rd rev. ed. 1935.

Meyer, B. S., and Anderson, D. B. *Plant Physiology*. New York: D. Van Nostrand Company, 2nd ed. 1952.

Nearing, G. G. *The Lichen Book*. Privately printed, 1947.

Parker, Bertha M., and Buchsbaum, Ralph. *Balance in Nature*. Evanston: Row, Peterson and Company, 1941.

Seifriz, William. *The Physiology of Plants*. New York: John Wiley and Son, 1941.

Shoosmith, F. H. *Life in the Animal World*. New York: Robert M. McBride and Company, 1937.

Teale, Edwin Way. *Grassroot Jungles*. New York: Dodd, Mead and Company, 1957.